Anguish Languish

Howard L. Chace

Alpha Editions

#

#

This Edition Published in 2021

ISBN: 9789355349491

Design and Setting By
Alpha Editions
www.alphaedis.com
Email – info@alphaedis.com

#

TABLE OF CONTENT

#

\#

INTRODUCTION

THE ANGUISH LANGUISH

English words are astonishingly versatile and could readily be made to serve a new and extraordinary purpose, but nobody seems to care about this except SPAL (Society for the Promotion of the Anguish Languish). In keeping with its lofty ideals and its slogan, ANGUISH FOR EVERYBODY, the Society is sponsoring this little text, which has three aims:

1. To improve the public's understanding of the Anguish Languish.

2. To improve the academic standing of the Anguish Languish.

3. To improve the social *and* financial standing of the Society.

☞ Policemen and Magicians

A visiting professor of Anguish, Dr. ——, who, while learning to understand spoken English, was continually bewildered and embarrassed by the similarity of such expressions as *boys and girls* and *poisoned gulls*, used to exclaim:

"Gracious! What a lot of words sound like each other! If it wasn't (*sic*) for the different situations in which we hear 'em, we'd have a terrible time saying which was which."

Of course, these may not have been the professor's exact words, because he often did his exclaiming in Anguish rather than in English. In that case he would say:

"*Crashes! Water larders warts sunned lack itch udder! Effervescent further deferent saturations an witch way harem, wade heifer haliver tam sang witch worse witch.*"

Dr. —— was right, both in English and Anguish. Although other factors than the pronunciation of words affect our ability to understand them, the situation in which the words are uttered is of prime importance. You can easily prove this, right in the privacy of your own kitchen, by asking a friend to help you wash up a dozen cops and sorcerers. Ten to one, she'll think you said a dozen *cups and saucers*, and be genuinely surprised if you put her to work cleaning up even *one* police officer, let alone all the others, and the magicians, too.

If you think that she misunderstands merely because the two phrases sound somewhat alike and *not* because of the situation, read what SPAL's Committee on Housewives has to say:

"Presented with a dishes-piled-in-sink situation, several hundred well-adjusted housewives thought that *cops and sorcerers* referred to dishes, but seldom did normal subjects, interviewed under the same conditions, make the opposite mistake. When they were asked to help us wash *cups and saucers*, some women consented, some made stupid excuses, and some told us bluntly to go wash them ourselves, but *practically no one thought that we were talking about policemen and magicians.*"

"Are empty mustard off mar fate

Are empty catsup off mouse hole."

What Anguish Really Is. 🐦

The experiments described above, and hundreds of similar ones conducted by SPAL show that *an unbelievable number of English words, regardless of their usual meanings, can be substituted quite satisfactorily for others.* When *all* the words in a given passage of English have been so replaced, the passage keeps its original meaning, but all the words have acquired new ones. *A word that has received a new meaning has become a* wart, *and when all the words in the passage have become warts, the passage is no longer English; it's* Anguish.

Are There Any Good Reasons to Study Anguish? 🐦

This is not an altogether silly question, and it deserves the prompt and unequivocal answer any Anguish Languish enthusiast will give it.

"Watcher mane, ardor rainy gut raisins toe sturdy anguish?" he will say, and will probably give you an impressive list of them which will certainly include the following:

1. Anguish is fun.

You and your friends can make a game out of learning Anguish, and you'll have fun developing your own style and observing each other's efforts. How to begin will be explained later.

2. Anguish Languish means verbal economy.

If words can be made to do double, triple, or even quadruple duty, it is obvious that we don't need so many of them. Wouldn't it be a comfort to know that, in the event of some unpredictable disaster wiping out half of our English vocabulary, we could, if we had learned Anguish, get along nicely with what we had left?

3. Anguish helps out in certain social situations.

People who aren't sure of themselves should learn Anguish. Suppose you have been asked to dinner by the president of your company and his wife. Since you haven't met your hostess, you have spent some time, before going, thinking up something to say that will really interest her. Finally you decide to ask, during the dinner:

"Mrs. Bellowell, didn't I hear that your brother Henry was discovered to be in collusion with those election crooks?"

The moment arrives, but you no sooner get her attention than you have sudden misgivings. Too late to change your subject, you slip deftly into Anguish:

"Mrs. Bellowell ... deaden are hair ditcher broader Hennery worse dish-cupboard toe bang collision wet dozer liquor-chin crocks?"

Chances are that everyone will be so fascinated by the graceful form of your question that not even your hostess will attach much importance to what you've asked.

EUROPE OILY DISK MOANING!

DOILY BOARD CASHES OR WARM!

4. Anguish relieves that terrible craving to tell dialect stories.

People who are addicted to telling dialect stories, or chronically frustrated because they can't tell them without Scotch brogue or Brooklynese getting mixed up with Deep South, will be overjoyed with Anguish. *Anguish is definitely* not *a dialect, since it consists* only *of unchanged English words which anyone can pronounce.* By imparting a delicate and indefinably exotic accent to one's speech, however, it not only provides a socially acceptable substitute for telling dialect stories, but adds to one's personal charm.

5. Anguish improves your English.

As your Anguish vocabulary increases, you'll find that your English vocabulary does, too, but you must be careful not to mix them up—something which people orphan do when they begin to use words accordion to the way they sound rather than how they're spelled. Words which are rare in English are often common enough in Anguish, so you have new opportunities to see them. Suppose you're spending a week-end reciting nursery rhymes in Anguish to a happy group of children or immature adults, and come across *SING A SONG OF SIXPENCE, A POCKET FULL OF RYE.* In Anguish, this, of course, is *SINKER SUCKER SOCKS PANTS, APOCRYPHAL AWRY.* This will give you an unexpected chance to use the last two words.

You'd be surprised to know how many people haven't the faintest idea what a xyster is until they hear a SPAL member talking about his fodder, murder, broader, and xyster. This makes them want to look *xyster* up. When they do, they find that, although *xyster* in Anguish, may mean *sister*, in English it's nothing in the world but a common raspatorium. Now raspatoria, and, therefore xysters are important surgical instruments, nice to know about before being scheduled for an aberration.

Speaking of xysters, hominy people know what *higglery* is? Very few, yet it occurs in the Anguish Languish version of something as well known as:

"Murder, mare argo art toe swarm?"

"Yap, mar doling dodder,

Hank yore clues honor higglery larme

An dun gore norther warder!"

While you're looking up *higglery*, you might find *larme*, just a few pages away in Webster's Unabridged.

"—wail, debt worse inner laest wake off Dismember—nor, inner foist wake off Janizary—Doctor Smatters (haze mar surging) gummier fun cull wan moaning, an set: 'Gut moaning, Messes Huffywate, heresy ladle bat noose furrier—yore garner heifer heifer nodder aberration.' Wail, whinny set debt—" etc., etc.

6. Practical Anguish.

Anguish can be used for group study at parties and entertainments; as a psychological test of something or other (we don't know just what), and as practice material in Speech and Typing classes.

How Can One Learn Anguish? ☜

1. Read everything in this text aloud, and preferably in a group. Make a game of it.

You'll find it easier to understand Anguish when you *hear* it than when you see it. If you have trouble, listen to someone else read it to you, preferably someone who doesn't quite know what he's reading. This often gives the best effect. Watch what happens when the listeners understand better than the reader.

2. Don't try to read too fast and be sure to give all words their usual English pronunciation, regardless of the new meaning the word has acquired. An accurate pronunciation and good intonation are most effective.

3. Don't worry if you seem to have suddenly acquired a slight accent; your friends will tell you that this is most attractive.

The members of SPAL are the persons who have written to the author concerning the Anguish Languish, especially the thousands who wrote to request copies of LADLE RAT ROTTEN HUT after Arthur Godfrey's inimitable reading of it, on his television show. The society is very poorly organized, in fact few of the members even know they belong. There are no officers, no meetings, no convention, and, worst of all, from the point of view of the author and founder, no dues.

This isn't his real name, nor is it intended to be the name of any other Anguish Languish professor, living or dead.

Whether or not such a calamity is likely to occur seems entirely beside the point; in times like these one should be prepared for any emergency.

ANGUISH ANONYMOUS, an organization of former dialect story tellers, sponsored by SPAL, can be called in difficult cases.

The plural of *xyster* in Anguish, is *cisterns*. See, in this book, the story of *Center Alley*.

A research psychologist plans to use *Anguish Languish* to provide data for a study entitled: "*Individual and Sex Differences in Configurational Perception of Artificially Contrived but Phenomenologically Comprehensible Auditory Stimuli.*" This sounds as if it should mean something.

The first item in this collection is a story familiar to all readers—LITTLE RED RIDING HOOD. Or, as you can probably say now in Anguish, LADLE RAT ROTTEN HUT.

Heresy ladle furry starry toiling udder warts—warts welcher altar girdle deferent firmer once inner regional virgin. This sentence means: "Here is a little fairy story told in other words—words which are altogether different from the ones in the original version."

ORIOLE RATTY? DEN LESS GAT STUTTERED!

1
FURRY TELLS
LADLE RAT ROTTEN HUT

Wants pawn term dare worsted ladle gull hoe lift wetter murder inner ladle cordage honor itch offer lodge, dock, florist. Disk ladle gull orphan worry putty ladle rat cluck wetter ladle rat hut, an fur disk raisin pimple colder Ladle Rat Rotten Hut.

Wan moaning Ladle Rat Rotten Hut's murder colder inset.

"Ladle Rat Rotten Hut, heresy ladle basking winsome burden barter an shirker cockles. Tick disk ladle basking tutor cordage offer groin-murder hoe lifts honor udder site offer florist. Shaker lake! Dun stopper laundry wrote! Dun stopper peck floors! Dun daily-doily inner florist, an yonder nor sorghum-stenches, dun stopper torque wet strainers!"

"Hoe-cake, murder," resplendent Ladle Rat Rotten Hut, an tickle ladle basking an stuttered oft.

Honor wrote tutor cordage offer groin-murder, Ladle Rat Rotten Hut mitten anomalous woof.

"Wail, wail, wail!" set disk wicket woof, "Evanescent Ladle Rat Rotten Hut! Wares are putty ladle gull goring wizard ladle basking?"

"Armor goring tumor groin-murder's," reprisal ladle gull. "Grammar's seeking bet. Armor ticking arson burden barter an shirker cockles."

"O hoe! Heifer gnats woke," setter wicket woof, butter taught tomb shelf, "Oil tickle shirt court tutor cordage offer groin-murder. Oil ketchup wetter letter, an den—O bore!"

Soda wicket woof tucker shirt court, an whinny retched a cordage offer groin-murder, picked inner windrow, an sore debtor pore oil worming worse lion inner bet. Inner flesh, disk abdominal woof lipped honor bet, paunched honor pore oil worming, an garbled erupt. Den disk ratchet ammonol pot honor groin-murder's nut cup an gnat-gun, any curdled ope inner bet.

Inner ladle wile, Ladle Rat Rotten Hut a raft attar cordage, an ranker dough ball. "Comb ink, sweat hard," setter wicket woof, disgracing is verse.

Ladle Rat Rotten Hut entity bet rum, an stud buyer groin-murder's bet.

"O Grammar!" crater ladle gull historically, "Water bag icer gut! A nervous sausage bag ice!"

"Battered lucky chew whiff, sweat hard," setter bloat-Thursday woof, wetter wicket small honors phase.

"O, Grammar, water bag noise! A nervous sore suture anomalous prognosis!"

"Battered small your whiff, doling," whiskered dole woof, ants mouse worse waddling.

"O Grammar, water bag mouser gut! A nervous sore suture bag mouse!"

Daze worry on-forger-nut ladle gull's lest warts. Oil offer sodden, caking offer carvers an sprinkling otter bet, disk hoard-hoarded woof lipped own pore Ladle Rat Rotten Hut an garbled erupt.

MURAL: Yonder nor sorghum stenches shut ladle gulls stopper torque wet strainers.

GUILTY LOOKS ENTER TREE BEERS

Wants pawn term dare worsted ladle gull hoe hat search putty yowler coils debt pimple colder Guilty Looks. Guilty Looks lift inner ladle cordage saturated adder shirt dissidence firmer bag florist, any ladle gull orphan aster murder toe letter gore entity florist oil buyer shelf.

"Guilty Looks!" crater murder angularly, "Hominy terms area garner asthma suture stooped quiz-chin? Goiter door florist? Sordidly NUT!"

"Wire nut, murder?" wined Guilty Looks, hoe dint peony tension tore murder's scaldings.

"Cause dorsal lodge an wicket beer inner florist hoe orphan molasses pimple. Ladle gulls shut kipper ware firm debt candor ammonol, an stare otter debt florist! Debt florist's mush toe dentures furry ladle gull!"

Wail, pimple oil-wares wander doe wart udder pimple dum wampum toe doe. Debt's jest hormone nurture. Wan moaning, Guilty Looks dissipater murder, an win entity florist.

Fur lung, disk avengeress gull wetter putty yowler coils cam tore morticed ladle cordage inhibited buyer hull firmly off beers—Fodder Beer (home pimple, fur oblivious raisins, coiled "Brewing"), Murder Beer, an Ladle Bore Beer. Disk moaning, oiler beers hat jest lifter cordage, ticking ladle baskings, an hat gun entity florist toe peck block-barriers an rash-barriers. Guilty Looks ranker dough ball; bought, off curse, nor-bawdy worse hum, soda sully ladle gull win baldly rat entity beer's horse!

Honor tipple inner darning rum, stud tree boils fuller sop—wan grade bag boiler sop, wan muddle-sash boil, an wan tawny ladle boil. Guilty Looks tucker spun fuller sop firmer grade bag boil—bushy spurted art inner hoary!

"Arch!" crater gull, "Debt sop's toe hart—barns mar mouse!"

Dingy traitor sop inner muddle-sash boil, witch worse toe coiled. Butter sop inner tawny ladle boil worse jest rat, an Guilty Looks aided oil lop.

Dingy nudist tree cheers—wan anomalous cheer, wan muddle-sash cheer, an wan tawny ladle cheer. Guilty Looks set darn inner ladle cheer, bushy worse toe bag ferret, ant soddenly bustard.

Clamming upper stars tutor beer's bet-rum, Guilty Looks dish-cupboard tree bets—wan grade bag bet, wan muddle-sash bet, an wan tawny ladle bet. Failing torrid, shay flunker shelf honor ladle bet, an, jester cobbler menace letter, worse sunder slip an snorting.

Inner ladle wile, donors offer cordage cam beck firmer barrier-pecking extradition, currying baskings fuller rash-barriers. Whinny entity darning rum, Fodder Beer stuttered snuffing an gruelling tomb shelf.

"Warts ban goring earn hair?" crumpled dole beer, "Conjure small psalm-sing deferent a boarder horse?"

"Crashes!" crater murder beer, ashy castor quack glands adder tipple, "Hose ban muddling wet debt sop?"

Ladle Bore Beer stuttered crayon.

"Jest locket mar ladle boiler sop—oil garbled dope! An locket mar itchy pitchy cheer—oil bustard!"

Locking adder bustard cheer, Murder Beer bay-gander gat historical, an stuttered hurling tore horsebarn:

"Brewing! Brewing! Way gut BURGHERS inner horse. HORSE BURGHERS! Quack! Coiler place! Wail, dun stun dare lacking end-bustle during nosing! Coiler Place Deportment, quack!"

"Harmer garner coiler Place Deportment wen way dun heifer toiler-fun?" resplendent Brewing, inner trampling verse. "Set darn, worming, an cape quoit! Yore oil-wares thanking dare burghers inner horse!"

Oiler shame, Brewing worse jesters scarred aster udders; infect, haze niece war shagging.

Finely, Fodder Beer gutter grade bag short-gum, Murder Beer gutter muddle-sash haunting raffle, an Ladle Bore Beer gutter tawny ladle pestle, an oiler beers crypt upper stars, ware Guilty Looks worse line honor bet, sunder slip an snorting. Herring door beers, shay weakened, lipped otter door windrow, an dished aware harm jesters fascist shagged scrabble.

Oiler beers tar darner stars, an stuttered toe locker doers an windrows.

"Fodder," aster ladle bore beer, finely, "Wart *worse* debt discussing crasher honor bet? Wart *worse* debt ogling ammonol wet oil debt yowler far honor had, an hoe dint half nor far atoll honor beck? Wart *worse* debt hobble lurking crasher, Fodder?"

Fodder Beer shuttered.

"Comb hair, mar bore. Heresy gut lessen furrier! Debt discussing crasher worsen HORMONE BANG! Kipper ware firm debt candor ammonol! Dare nor gut! Warts mar, are dun wander catcher goring entity florist oil bar yore shelf. *Debt florist's mush toe dentures furry ladle beer!*"

CENTER ALLEY

Center Alley worse jester pore ladle gull hoe lift wetter stop-murder an toe heft-cisterns. Daze worming war furry wicket an shellfish parsons, spatially dole stop-murder, hoe dint lack Center Alley an, infect, word orphan traitor pore gull mar lichen ammonol dinner hormone bang. Oily inner moaning disk wicket oiled worming shorted, "Center Alley, gad otter bet, an goiter wark! Suture lacy ladle bomb! Shaker lake!" an firm moaning tell gnat disk ratchet gull word heifer wark lacquer hearse toe kipper horsing ardor, washer heft-cistern's closing, maker bets, gore tutor star fur perversions, cooker males, washer dashes an doe oily udder hoard wark. Nor wander pore Center Alley worse tarred an disgorged!

Wan moaning, Center Alley herder heft-cisterns tucking a boarder bag boil debtor prance worse garner gift toiler pimple inner lend.

"O stop-murder," crater ladle gull, "Water swill cerebration debt boil's garner bay! Are sordidly ward lacquer goiter debt boil!"

"Shed dope, Center Alley," inserter curl stop-murder, "Yore tucking lichen end-bustle! Yore nutty goring tore debt boil—*armor* goring tutor boil wet yore toe heft-cisterns. Yore garner stair rat hair, an kipper horsing ardor an washer pods an pens! Gore tutor boil? Hoar, hoar! Locket yore close—nosing bought racks!"

Soda wicket stop-murder any toe ogling cisterns pot honor expansive closing, an stuttered oft tutor boil, living pore Center Alley setting buyer far inner racket closing, wit tares strumming darner chicks.

Soddenly, Center Alley nudist debt annulled worming hat entity rum, an worse setting buyer site. Disk oiled worming worry furry gourd-murder.

"Center Alley, Center Alley," whiskered dole worming, "watcher crane aboard? Ditcher wander goiter debt boil? Hoe-cake, jest goiter yore gardening an pickle bag pomp-can; den goiter yore staple an gutter bag rattletrap witch contends sex anomalous ratch. Wail, watcher wading fur? Gat goring!"

Center Alley garter pomp-can any sex bag ratch. Inner flesh, dole worming chintz door pomp-can intern anomalous, gorges, courage. Dingy chintz door sex beg ratch enter sex wide hearses. Oil offer sodden, Center Alley real-iced dashy worse warring putty an expansive closing—sulk an sadden—an honor ladle fate war toe putty ladle gloss slobbers.

Center Alley, harpy acid lurk, clammed entity gorges courage, any sex wide hearses gobbled aware tutor prance's boil.

"O bore!" crater prance, whinny sore Center Alley, "Hoes disk putty ladle checking wetter gloss slobbers?" any win ope toe Center Alley an aster furry dense, den fur servile udders. Door prance dint wander dense wet dodder gulls—jest wet Center Alley.

Pimple whiskered, "Jest locket debt gnats-lurking cobble! Door prance sordidly enter-stance harder peck gut-lurking worming!"

Ladle Center Alley worse door bail offer boil.

Door wicket stop-murder any toe ogling cisterns wore trampling wet anchor an forestation.

"Courses, courses!" crater stop-murder. "Hoes debt ladle Manx wetter gloss slobbers? A nervous sore suture ladle horsey, any prance axe lackeys knots a barter! Lucks lackeys garner dense wetter oil gnat, wile oil ware during aster set hair an kipper cheers worm! Courses!"

Oil offer sodden door cluck stork mit-gnat. Inner flesh, Center Alley's putty closing chintz backer racks, enter pore gull hatter dasher ware firmer boil. Goring donor steers, Center Alley caked offer ladle gloss slobber. Door prance traitor casher, bought oily gut worse door slobber.

Necks moaning door Prance set: "Arm goring toe fine debt putty gull hoe worse warring disk slobber. Shale bay mar waif, debt's fur shore, an oil bare horsebarn."

Den, lipping honors hearse, door prance gobbled aware.

Whinny prance retched Center Alley's horse, door stop-murder an toe heft-cisterns wandered toe traitor pot honor gloss slobber.

"Arch, arch! Debt hearts!" crater cisterns. "Are fates toe bag fur debt slobber!"

"Arch, arch! Ticket oft!" shorted door stop-murder, "Wart inhale yore during, Prance? Debt slobber's toe ladle furry hormone bang! Ticket oft!"

Wile ticking offer slobber, door prance nudist Center Alley setting buyer far, any set: "Hoes debt ratchet ladle crasher? Props debt pore gull cut pot honor gloss slobber."

Door abdominal stop-murder any toe wicket heft-cisterns bust art luffing.

"Hoar, hoar, hoar! Debt's jest Center Alley. Yore wooden wander half suture discussing parson furry waif! Lock attar hens and phase—oil cupboard wet dart! Locket doze close—nosing bought racks!"

"Jester seam," resplendent door prance, gadding impassioned, "arm garner traitor pot disk slobber honor ladle fort. Comb hair, Center Alley."

Wail, bores and gulls, badger canned gas wart hopping! Center Alley tickle ladle slobber an potted earn. Den, oil offer sodden, door prance potters alms rounder ladle gull an caster—rat honor mouse!

Fur lung, wadding balls war wrangling, an Center Alley winter wear firmer wicket stop-murder's horse, an becalm door mattress offer prance's gorges mention. Center Alley worse jest knots aboard disk hansom horsebarn, an lift, yonder daze harpy sorghum-stenches, furry lung, lung, tam.

MURAL: Ladle gulls shunt bay disgorged; warts garner hoppings garner hopping.

2
NOISIER RAMS
MARRY HATTER LADLE LIMB

Marry hatter ladle limb

Itch fleas worse widest snore.

An ever-wear debt Marry win

Door limb worse shorter gore.

SINKER SUCKER SOCKS PANTS

Sinker sucker socks pants

Apocryphal awry

Foreign turnkey blank boards

Bagged inner pyre.

Whinny pious orphaned

Door boards bay-gander sink.

Worsen dizzy jelly ditch

Toe setter furry kink?

Door kink worse inner conning horse

Conning otters moaning.

Door coin worse inner panda

Aiding burden honing.

Door mate worse inner gardening

Hankering ardor cloys.

A lung camel blank board

An sniffed offer noise!

EFFERVESCENT

Effervescent further ACHE

dare wooden bather CHECKING.

Effervescent further PEG

way wooden heifer BECKING.

Effervescent further LESSENS

dare wooden bather DITCHERS.

Effervescent further ODDEST

way wooden heifer PITCHERS

Effervescent further CLASHES

way wooden kneader CLASH RUMS.

Effervescent further BASH TOPS

way wooden heifer BASH RUMS.

Effervescent further TUCKING

way wooden heifer LANGUISH.

Effervescent fur daze phony WARTS

nor bawdy cud spick ANGUISH!

OILED MURDER HARBORED

Oiled Murder Harbored

Wen tutor cardboard

Toe garter pore darker born.

Wenchy gut dare

Door cardboard worse bar

An soda pore dark hat known.

PITTER PAPER

Pitter Paper peeked or parker peckled paupers

Or packer peckled paupers pitter paper peeked

Aft Pitter Paper peeked or packer peckled paupers

Ware aster packer peckled paupers debt pitter paper peeked?

3
FEY-MOUSE TELLS
CASING ADDER BET

Oh, somewhere in this favored land the sun is shining bright;

The band is playing somewhere, and somewhere hearts are light,

And somewhere men are laughing, and somewhere children shout;

But there is no joy in Mudville—mighty Casey has struck out.

ERNEST LAWRENCE THAYER

Heresy borsch-boil starry a boarder borsch boil gam plate lung, lung a gore inner ladle wan hearse torn coiled Mutt-fill.

Mutt-fill worsen mush offer torn, butted hatter putty gut borsch-boil tame, an off oiler pliers honor tame, door moist cerebrated worse Casing. Casing worsted sickened basement, any hatter betting orphanage off .526 (punt fife toe sex).

Casing worse gut lurking, an furry poplar—spatially wetter gull coiled Any-bally. Any-bally worse Casing's sweat-hard, any harpy cobble wandered toe gat merit, bought Casing worse toe pore toe becalm Any-bally's horsebarn, (Boil pliers honor Mutt-fill tame dint gat mush offer celery; infect, day gut nosing atoll.)

Bought less gat earn wetter starry.

Wan dare, inner Mutt-fill borsch boil pork, door scar stud lack disk inner lest in-ink:

MUTT-FILL   2

UDDER TAME   4

Water disgorging saturation! Oiler Mutt-fill rotors setting inner grin-stance, war failing furry darn inner mouse.

Bought, watcher thank hopping? Soddenly wan offer Mutt-fill pliers hitter shingle, an an-udder plier gutter gnats toe beggar! Soda war ptomaine earn basis. Bust off oil, Casing ham-shelf, Mutt-fill's cerebrated better, worse combing ope toe bet!

Whinny kraut inner grin-stance sore Casing combing, day stuttered toe clabber hens an yowl, "Dare's CASING! Attar bore, Casing!" An whinny hansom sickened basement sundered confidentially ope tutor plat, oiler Mutt-fill rotors shorted:

"CASING ROAR!
CASING ROAR!
ROAR, ROAR, CASING!"

Putty ladle Any-bally, setting oil buyer shelf inner grin-stance, worse furry prod offer gut lurking loafer. Lack oiler udder pimple, Any-bally worse shore debt Casing worse garner winner boil gam fur Mutt-fill.

Casing weaved tutor kraut, an castor sweat glands add Any-bally, den retched darn tutor grunt an robbed dart honors hens, an warped haze hens honors pence.

"PLY BOIL!" shorted door empire, gadding impassioned.

Casing pecked upper bet, an locked adder patcher, any set tomb shelf:

"Latter comb! Arm garner smirk disk boil rat offer defense!"

ZOMBIE! Door boil short pest Casing lacquer canning boil. Casing dint peony tension turret.

"STORK WARN!" crater empire.

Door kraut inner grin-stance stuttered shorting an coursing.

"Wart inhale's madder wet debt empire's ICE? Hazy gun BLAND?"

"Lessen, empire—Java heifer ICE exempted? Batter goiter seeder obstetrician!"

"Boor! Boor! B-o-o-r!"

"O water bag BOMB!"

Door patcher warn dope akin, any boil short pest Casing lacquer bullock firmer raffle.

"STORK TOE!" setter empire, lurking unctuously adder kraut.

Oiler Mutt-fill fens an rotors war hurling wet anchor! Servile bear bordels an corker cooler bordels cam firmer grin-stance, an fail honor grunt, nut for firmer pore empire's fate.

Inner grin-stance, ladle Any-bally, hoe dint lacquer seer loafer mucker bag foal otter ham-shelf, bay-gander wiper ice wetter tawny ladle lazy hanker-sniff.

Wants akin, Casing locked adder patcher, disk term wetter lock off gram razor-lotion honors phase.

"Jest locket Casing!" whiskered door kraut, "Disk term, Casing manes baseness. Badger Casing's garner smirk debt borsch-boil rat offer defense!"

SWASH! Casing swank adder boil wet oilers farce! Water swank! Wart anomalous farce! Wart gram razor-lotion!

Water sham debt Casing dint hitter boil!

"Stork tree—yore art!" whiskered door empire, trampling, an gadding ratty toe dock corker cooler bordels an bear bordels.

Door kraut worse stunt.

Any-bally worse sopping historically inner tawny ladle lazy hanker-sniff.

Wail, yawl nor debt putty pacer pottery coiled CASING ADDER BET—spatially doze lest melon-colic versus:

"*O psalm-war an disk fevered lend, door soreness shunning brat;*

Door benders plying psalm-war, an psalm-war hurts alite,

An psalm-war manor luffing, an psalm-war chaldron short;

Butter ash nor jarring Mutt-fill—muddy Casing hash stork art!"

Bought lessen, forks! Wander nor wart *rally* hopping? Wail, doze putty versus becalm cerebrated—an Casing becalm cerebrated, toe! Suture bag kraut off pimple cam toe Mutt-fill toe shag hens wetter hansom borsch boil plier debt Casing win enter parlor-tricks, an gat retch. An, whinny gut retch (conjure gas?) Casing becalm door diverted horsebarn off putty ladle Any-bally.

Violate Huskings
ore
Ornery Aboard Inner Gelded Ketch

POT 1
Darn Honor Form

Heresy rheumatic starry offer former's dodder, Violate Huskings, an wart hoppings darn honor form.

Violate lift wetter fodder, oiled Former Huskings, hoe hatter repetition fur bang furry retch—an furry stenchy. Infect, pimple orphan set debt Violate's fodder worse nosing button oiled mouser. Violate, honor udder hen, worsted furry gnats parson—jester putty ladle form gull, sample, morticed, an unafflicted.

Wan moaning Former Huskings nudist haze dodder setting honor cheer, during nosing.

"VIOLATE!" shorted dole former, "Watcher setting darn fur? Denture nor yore canned gat retch setting darn during nosing? Germ pup otter debt cheer!"

"Arm tarred, Fodder," resplendent Violate warily.

"Watcher tarred fur?" aster stenchy former, hoe dint half mush symphony further gull. "Are badger dint doe mush woke disk moaning! Ditcher curry doze buckles fuller slob darn tutor peg-pan an feeder pegs?"

"Yap, Fodder. Are fetter pegs."

"Ditcher mail-car caws an swoop otter caw staple?"

"Off curse, Fodder. Are mulct oiler caws an swapped otter staple, an fetter checkings, an clammed upper larder inner checking-horse toe gadder oiler aches, an wen darn tutor vestibule guarding toe peck oiler bogs an warms offer vestibules, an watched an earned yore closing, an fetter hearses an...."

"Ditcher *warder* oiler hearses, toe?" enter-ruptured oiled Huskings.

"Nor, Fodder, are dint."

"Dint warder mar hearses? Wire nut?"

"Arm surrey, Fodder, butcher hearses jest worsen Thursday. Yore kin leader hearse toe warder, Fodder, butcher cannon maggot drank. Lessen, Fodder, arm tarred!"

"Oil-wares tarred!" crumpled Huskings. "Wail, sense yore sore tarred, oil lecher wrestle ladle, bought GAD OFFER DEBT CHEER! Wile yore wrestling, yore kin maker bets an washer dashes."

Suture fodder! Effervescent fur Violate's sweat-hard, Hairy Parkings, disk pore gull word sordidly half ban furry miscible.

POT 2
Moan-late an Roaches

Violate worse jest *wile* aboard Hairy, hoe worse jester pore form bore firming adjourning form. Sum pimple set debt Hairy Parkings dint half gut since, butter hatter gut dispossession an hay worse medley an luff wet Violate. Infect, Hairy wandered toe merrier, butter worse toe skirt toe aster.

Wan gnat Hairy an Violate war setting honor Huskings' beck perch inner moan-late, holing hens.

"O Hairy," crate Violate, "Jest locket debt putty moan! Arsenate rheumatic?"

"Yap," inserted Hairy, lurking adder moan.

"O Hairy," contingent Violate, "Jest snuff doze flagrant orders combing firmer putty rat roaches inner floor guarding! Conjure small doze orders, Hairy? Conjure small debt deletitious flagrancy?"

"Yap," set Hairy, snuffing, lacquer haunting dug haunting fur rapids.

"Lessen, Hairy," whiskered Violate, "Arm ... arm oil-moist *shore* yore gut sum-sing toe asthma. Denture half sum-sing impertinent toe asthma, Hairy? Denture?"

Pore Hairy, skirt oil-moist artifice wets, stuttered toe trample, butter poled ham-shelf toe-gadder, an gargled:

"Ark ... yap, Violate ... are gas ... are gas are gut sum-sing ... O shocks, Violate!"

"Gore earn, Hairy, gore earn!" encysted Violate, gadding impassioned. "Dun bay sore inhabited! Nor, den, watcher garner asthma?"

"Wail, Violate, arm jester pore form bore, an dun half mush moaning...."

"Hoe cars aboard moaning, Hairy? Pimple dun heifer bay retch toe gat merit, bought day order *lack* itch udder. Merit cobbles hoe *lack* itch udder gadder lung mush batter den udder cobbles hoe *dun* lack itch udder. Merit pimple order bay *congenital*, an arm *shore*, Hairy, debt wail bay *furry* congenital an contended, an, fur debt raisin, way dun heifer half mush moaning."

Furry lung, lung, term disk harpy cobble set honor beck perch inner moan-late, holing hens an snuffing flagrant orders firmer floors inner floor guarding. Finely Violate set:

"Bought lessen, Hairy—inner moaning yore gutter asthma fodder."

Radar, conjure gas wart hopping? Hairy aster fodder, hoe exploited wet anchor, an setter larder furry bat warts. Infect, haze languish worse jest hobble. Yonder nor sorghum-stenches wad disk stenchy oiled mouser lettuce dodder asepsis pore bore furry horsebarn. Hairy, shagging wetter motion, toll Violate water fodder hat set.

"Dun bay disgorged," set Violate. "Wail jest waiter wile. Pimple hoe wander gat merit gutter half passions."

POT 3
Evanescent Wan Think Itching Udder.

Wan moaning, servile wicks letter, Violate worse inner fodder's vestibule guarding darn honor hens an niece, pecking bogs an warms offer vestibules. Soddenly shay nudist annulled badger-lore, home pimple cold "Carnal" Gatretch, combing entity guarding. (Gatretch worsen rallier carnal—hay worse jester retch oiled stork-barker hoed madder mullion dullards soiling storks an barns, an hoe lift inner palatal an luxuriant mention nut fur firmer Huskings' form.)

"Gut moaning, Carnal Gatretch," set Violate respectively. "Europe oily disk moaning."

"Doily board cashes a warm!" resplendent Gatretch wetter wicket charcoal. "Arming oily board—an yore jester putty ladle warm."

"Arm shore yore jest jerking, Carnal," setter gull, wetter morticed blotch, "Warts mar, arm nutty warm—arm Violate Huskings."

"Nutty warm?" aster carnal, "Den watcher during darn honor hens an niece inner mutton dart? O water sham, water sham, debt search putty ladle wide hens shut bay oil cupboard wet mutton dart! Comb hair, Violate! Lessee doze putty ladle hens! *Arm* garner trait doze hens mar respectively."

"Jest warts yore porpoise, Carnal?" aster gull. "Jest watcher incinerating?"

"Conjure gas mar porpoise, doling?" whiskered dole stork-barker. "Conjure gas wart arm incinerating? Wail, arm nutty garner baiter rounder borsch. Heresy hull think inner nuptial—arm garner gat merit, an *yore* garner bay Messes Gatretch. Yore gamer heifer palatal an luxuriant mention an storks an barns any cobble off Cattle-hacks, an yule bay warring manx an udder gorges closing, an damnings an perils an udder jowls...."

Violate shuttered.

"Kip yore manx an damnings an perils an udder retches, Carnal! Are dun wampum! Are dun wander merry nor-bawdy sceptor manor luff—an debt's Hairy Parkings!"

"Hairy Parkings!" crumpled Gatretch, wetter snare honors phase, "Watcher wander merry debt end-bustle fur? Hairy's jester bomb!"

Trampling wet indication, Violate stupid darn, pecked upper bag hen-furl off dart an flunk disk dart rat inner oiled stork-barker's phase!

"Gat otter mar fodder's vestibule guarding!" crater gull. "An dun comb beck!"

"Hoe-cake, hoe-cake," murdered Gatretch, "bought lessen hair, gull, yore garner heifer changer mine! Arm garner torque baseness wet yore fodder. Arm garner muck yore fodder servile ladle prepositions. An *arm garner bay yore horsebarn!*"

Fleshed wet anchor, an crumpling tomb-shelf, Gatretch win beck tutor Huskings' horse toe torque tutor stenchy oiled mouser.

POT 4
Wadding Balls an Better Tares.

Dole stork-barker worse rat. Former Huskings ascended tutor carnal's wicket preposition, an fur lung, Violate, sopping historically, an wet better tares strumming darner chicks, worse becalming Messes Gatretch. Censor fodder worse toe stenchy toe heifer wadding, Violate enter Carnal war stunning inner orifice offer Jesters offer Pace, lessening tutor jesters raiding doze fetal warts:

"Carnal, door yore tick disk worming furrier awful waif?"

("Shore," setter stork-barker.)

"Violate, door yore tick disk carnal furrier awful horsebarn?"

("Y-Yap," set Violate, sopping historically.)

Pimple shirker hets an set:

"Water sham! Suture putty gull an suture disherpated oiled badger-lore! Suture think shunt hopping tore gnats gull lack Violate!"

"Pore Violate! Violate's garner bay ornery aboard inner gelded ketch!"

Hairy Parkings worse melon-colic, butter worsen disgorged, any set tomb-shelf:

"Carnal Gatretch's jester cat-napper hoe cat-napped mar sweat-hard. Wail, jest waiter wile—props Hairy Parkings kin doer ladle cat-napping ham-shelf."

Servile wicks pest.

Wan dock gnat, wile Violate's horsebarn worse aware honor baseness trap, Hairy gutter lung larder, an clammed ope toe Violate's bet-rum windrow.

"Violate!" Hairy whiskered. "Germ pup! Itch yore loafer! Itch Hairy!"

Violate, herring debt farm-oilier verse, lipped otter bet, pot honor putty ladle bet-rum slobbers, an expansive four-laned, hen-an-bordered horse-court, an cam tutor windrow.

"Lessen, Violate," set Hairy, "Armor goring aware. Armor goring tumor groin-murder's form, darning Messy-soupy, an armor garner peck carton fur mar groin-murder. Peck yore begs, Violate! Gad otter disk gelded ketch! Clam darner larder, an wail goiter garter dam toe Messy-soupy!"

Furry mint, Violate dint yonder-stander loafer's preposition, den, wetter harpy, harpy, lurk honor phase, shay set:

"Yore rat, Hairy. Arm jester pore ladle retch gull—ornery aboard inner gelded ketch. Bought O bore! Water SWILL ketch! Dun heifer feeder pegs! Dun heifer mail-car caws an swoop otter caw staple! Dun heifer feeder checkings an gadder aches an peck warms offer vestibules! Dun heifer doe nor watching an earning, dun heifer warder hearses an maker bets an washer dashes! Door yore thank armor garner flier ware firm oil disk lechery? Known date! Sordidly nut! An lessen, Hairy; heresy ladle gut adverse: Wile yore darning Messy-soupy, dun stutter peck carton furrier groin-murder. Kipper *ware* firmer form, an finer swill possession inner stork-barker's orifice. Soil storks an barns, an maggot mullion dullards. DEN comb beck tumor windrow wet yore larder!"

4
LATH THING THUMB THONGS!
FRYER JERKER

Fryer Jerker, Fryer Jerker,

Dormer-view? Dormer-view?

Sunny lay martini!

Sunny lay martini!

Drink, drank, drunk.

Drink, drank, drunk.

ALLEY WETTER

Alley wetter, jaunty alley wetter,

Alley wetter, shutter plumber ray.

Shutter plumber railer tat

Shutter plumber railer tat

Ale a tat, ale a tat

Ale a tat, ale a tat

O,

Alley wetter, jaunty alley wetter,

Alley wetter, shutter plumber ray.

DOOR OIL GORY MAYOR

Odor oil gory mayor, shay ant washy oyster bay

Ant washy oyster bay,

Ant washy oyster bay!

Door oil gory mayor, shay ant washy oyster bay

Money lung yares a gore!

DARE ASHY TURBAN INNER TORN

Dare ashy turban inner torn, inner torn

An dare mar dare luff set shim darn, set shim darn

An drakes haze whine wet lefter fray

An nabber, nabber thanks off may.

Farther wail fur arm moist leaf year,

Doughnut letter parroting grave year,

Enter member debtor bust off fronts moist port, moist port.

Adjure, adjure, canned fronts, adjure, adjure, adjure;

Are kin nor lunger stare wet your, stare wet your.

Oil hank mar hop honor warping wallow tray,

An murder whirl gore wail wet they.

FUR HAZY JELLY GUT FURLOUGH

Fur hazy jelly gut furlough

Fur hazy jelly gut furlough

Fur hazy jelly gut furlough

Witch nor bawdy candor nigh

HIVE BAN WALKING HONOR ROIL RUT

Hive ban walking honor roil rut

Oiler laugh lung dare;

Hive ban walking honor roil rut

Jester pester tam aware.

Conjure herder weasels blurring,

Blurring sore oily inner moan?

Conjure herder chaldron shorting,

Diner want chew blur debt hone?

HURL, HURL, DOOR GONG'S OIL HAIR

Hurl, hurl, door gong's oil hair!

Moisten satyr knotty wart!

Moisten satyr knotty wart!

Hurl, hurl, door gong's oil hair!

Wart inhale dough way cur, nor?

HORMONE DERANGE

O gummier hum warder buffer-lore rum
Enter dare enter envelopes ply,
Ware soiled'em assured adage cur-itching ward
An disguise earn it clotty oil die.

Harm, hormone derange,
Warder dare enter envelopes ply,
Ware soiled'em assured adage cur-itching ward
An disguise earn it clotty oil die.